My MUSIC PRACTICE

Exclusive Distributors:
Music Sales Limited
Distribution Centre, Newmarket Road, Bury St Edmunds,
Suffolk IP33 3YB, UK.
Music Sales Pty Limited
20 Resolution Drive, Caringbah, NSW 2229, Australia.

Printed in the EU.

Edited by Rachel Lindley
Assistant Editors: Lizzie Moore & Oliver Miller
Cover design and book illustrations by Lizzie Barrand

Your Guarantee of Quality:
As publishers, we strive to produce every book to
the highest commercial standards.
Particular care has been given to specifying acid-free, neutral-sized
paper made from pulps which have not been elemental chlorine bleached.
This pulp is from farmed sustainable forests and was
produced with special regard for the environment.
Throughout, the printing and binding have been planned to
ensure a sturdy, attractive publication which should give years of enjoyment.
If your copy fails to meet our high standards,
please inform us and we will gladly replace it.

This book belongs to...

stick a picture
of yourself here!

Name _____

Age _____

Year _____

School _____

Teacher's contact details

_____

_____

_____

_____

Shopping List

Book title/Accessory	Publisher/Code
....	....
....	....
....	....
....	....
....	....
....	....
....	....
....	....
....	....
....	....
....	....
....	....
....	....
....	....
....	....
....	....

Contents

Practice Tips & Tricks

1. Set aside some time each day to ensure that you practise regularly.

2. Find a quiet place to practise so you don't have any distractions.

3. Don't always practise from the beginning of a piece, try working on the detail first.

4. Work on the bits you can't do, not just the bits you can!

5. Each time you practise, make sure you refer to your notebook and follow your teacher's comments and suggestions.

6. Play for family and friends and also with other musicians. It is fun and will help you become a better musician.

7. Remember to stand or sit in the right position and hold your instrument correctly.

8. Make sure you have the correct equipment you need for lessons and practice, such as a pencil, your Practice Notebook, your music, and your instrument!

9. Look after your instrument. After practising, clean it and put it away safely.

10. Before leaving your lesson check with your teacher that you understand what must be practised.

Lesson 1

Work to do:

Scales/Studies:

Pieces:

Practice record

	MON	TUES	WED	THURS	FRI	SAT	SUN
Scales/Studies							
Pieces							

My comments

Parent's/Carer's comments

Signature_____

Why was Mozart lost?

Because his teacher was Haydn

Lesson 2

Date/Time:

Work to do:

Scales/Studies:

Pieces:

Practice record

	Mon	Tues	Wed	Thurs	Fri	Sat	Sun
Scales/Studies							
Pieces							

My comments

Parent's/Carer's comments

Signature_____

In which key do most toilets flush?

Eb major

Lesson 3

Work to do:

Scales/Studies:

Pieces:

Practice record

	Mon	Tues	Wed	Thurs	Fri	Sat	Sun
Scales/Studies							
Pieces							

My comments

Parent's/Carer's comments

Signature_____

*Why do musicians have to be awake
by five o'clock?
Because most shops close by 5:30*

13

Lesson 4

Work to do:

Scales/Studies:

Pieces:

Practice record

	MON	TUES	WED	THURS	FRI	SAT	SUN
Scales/Studies							
Pieces							

My comments

Parent's/Carer's comments

Signature_____

Which composer was nicknamed 'The Red Priest'?
Antonio Vivaldi (1668–1741)

Lesson 5

Work to do:

Scales/Studies:

Pieces:

Practice record

	MON	TUES	WED	THURS	FRI	SAT	SUN
Scales/Studies							
Pieces							

My comments

Parent's/Carer's comments

Signature_____

Which is the most musical bone?

The Trombone

Lesson 6

Work to do:

Scales/Studies:

Pieces:

Practice record

	Mon	Tues	Wed	Thurs	Fri	Sat	Sun
Scales/Studies							
Pieces							

My comments

Parent's/Carer's comments

Signature_____

Take A Break!

Wordsearch

Use the images on the left, to help you find the words in the wordsearch on the right.

R	T	E	P	M	U	R	T	L	A	L	D	Q	G	E
T	E	F	K	T	R	O	M	B	O	N	E	C	L	O
A	C	Y	E	T	O	I	H	E	P	H	H	E	N	V
R	R	S	Y	L	N	P	O	E	N	C	C	F	M	I
T	N	H	B	E	D	A	A	I	O	T	R	U	N	O
S	N	R	O	H	H	C	N	E	R	F	D	A	F	L
G	U	H	A	Y	I	C	R	I	N	T	P	T	O	I
S	R	G	R	R	M	A	C	P	O	M	P	S	T	N
T	O	T	D	A	B	G	H	E	I	L	B	T	U	E
T	U	B	A	Y	U	G	G	T	E	A	A	R	M	T
L	Q	U	N	I	U	E	A	M	D	J	S	K	E	Y
D	B	V	T	L	K	I	T	E	R	P	S	L	O	T
S	H	A	U	C	S	Z	C	E	L	L	O	E	I	L
L	R	C	I	Y	O	T	R	E	A	F	O	P	H	H
A	S	T	R	T	H	A	N	D	E	R	N	S	H	F
B	T	A	R	S	O	A	F	F	R	C	O	L	P	L
M	I	B	B	O	L	E	R	D	D	O	S	C	K	U
Y	R	L	N	B	I	E	O	P	A	R	I	B	E	T
C	L	A	R	I	N	E	T	T	R	O	T	A	N	E
O	I	N	E	D	R	O	S	A	C	A	R	A	M	D

21

Lesson 7

Work to do:

Scales/Studies:

Pieces:

Practice record

	MON	TUES	WED	THURS	FRI	SAT	SUN
Scales/Studies							
Pieces							

My comments

Parent's/Carer's comments

Signature_____

What do you get when you drop a piano down a mine shaft?

A flat minor

Lesson 8

Work to do:

Scales/Studies:

Pieces:

Practice record

	Mon	Tues	Wed	Thurs	Fri	Sat	Sun
Scales/Studies							
Pieces							

My comments

Parent's/Carer's comments

Signature_____

In which city was George Frideric Handel's Messiah first performed?

Dublin (in 1742)

Lesson 9

Date/Time:

Work to do:

Scales/Studies:

Pieces:

Practice record

	MON	TUES	WED	THURS	FRI	SAT	SUN
Scales/Studies							
Pieces							

My comments

Parent's/Carer's comments

Signature_____

Why was the musician staring at the orange juice bottle?
Because the label said concentrate

Lesson 10

Date/Time:

Work to do:

Scales/Studies:

Pieces:

Practice record

	MON	TUES	WED	THURS	FRI	SAT	SUN
Scales/Studies							
Pieces							

My comments

Parent's/Carer's comments

Signature_____

What are the seven Greek modes?
Ionian – Dorian – Phrygian – Lydian –
Mixolydian – Aeolian – Locrian

Lesson 11

Work to do:

Scales/Studies:

Pieces:

Practice record

	MON	TUES	WED	THURS	FRI	SAT	SUN
Scales/Studies							
Pieces							

My comments

Parent's/Carer's comments

Signature_____

What do you call a gnome who lives in the city?

A metronome

Lesson 12

Work to do:

Scales/Studies:

Pieces:

Practice record

	MON	TUES	WED	THURS	FRI	SAT	SUN
Scales/Studies							
Pieces							

My comments

Parent's/Carer's comments

Signature_____

Who set the poem 'The Dream of Gerontius'
(by Cardinal John Henry Newman) to music?

Edward Elgar (1857–1964)

Take A Break!

Name That Tune
Play the tune and see if you recognise it...

1.

_____

2.

_____

3.

_____

4.

5.

6.

Some of these you may need to transpose, as the clef will not be suited to your instrument. Have a go and see if you can work it out on your own...

Lesson 13

Work to do:

Scales/Studies:

Pieces:

Practice record

	MON	TUES	WED	THURS	FRI	SAT	SUN
Scales/Studies							
Pieces							

My comments

Parent's/Carer's comments

Signature_____

How do you become a millionaire playing jazz?

Start off as a billionaire!

Lesson 14

Date/Time:

Work to do:

Scales/Studies:

Pieces:

Practice record

	Mon	Tues	Wed	Thurs	Fri	Sat	Sun
Scales/Studies							
Pieces							

My comments

Parent's/Carer's comments

Signature_____

Which pop star paid over a million pounds for the Steinway piano on which John Lennon wrote the song 'Imagine'?

George Michael (1963–)

Lesson 15

Date/Time:

Work to do:

Scales/Studies:

Pieces:

Practice record

	MON	TUES	WED	THURS	FRI	SAT	SUN
Scales/Studies							
Pieces							

My comments

Parent's/Carer's comments

Signature_____

A crescendo is a reminder for the musician
that they have been playing too loudly!

Lesson 16

Work to do:

Scales/Studies:

Pieces:

Practice record

	MON	TUES	WED	THURS	FRI	SAT	SUN
Scales/Studies							
Pieces							

My comments

Parent's/Carer's comments

Signature_____

In Switzerland, what is it illegal to do whilst dressed as Elvis Presley?

Mow the lawn

43

Lesson 17

Work to do:

Scales/Studies:

Pieces:

Practice record

	MON	TUES	WED	THURS	FRI	SAT	SUN
Scales/Studies							
Pieces							

My comments

Parent's/Carer's comments

Signature_____

What do you get if you combine diminished and augmented chords? Demented chords

Lesson 18

Work to do:

Scales/Studies:

Pieces:

Practice record

	MON	TUES	WED	THURS	FRI	SAT	SUN
Scales/Studies							
Pieces							

My comments

Parent's/Carer's comments

Signature_____

In what year did the first Proms concert take place in London?

1895

Take A Break!

Crossword

Use the clues on the right to complete the crossword.

Across

1. A scale of semitones (from the Greek word for colour) (9)
7. *Do, Re, Mi, Fa, So, ..., Ti* (2)
8. The Italian term for *sweet, soft* (5)
9. ♭ (4)
11. A song to send you to sleep (7)
13. *All, everyone* – a term commonly used in orchestral scores (5)
14. Early Jazz style e.g. Scott Joplin (7)
16. Tone quality/colour (6)
18. Two performers (3)
19. Phrase which means *from the beginning* (2, 4)
20. ...... signature – specifies the number of beats in a bar (4)

Down

1. Circular metal part of a drum kit, e.g. hi-hat/crash/ride (6)
2. The mouth-piece of an oboe (4)
3. Key change (10)
4. The Overture is the most famous part of this opera by Rossini, "William ....." (4)
5. Symbol at the beginning of a stave, used to indicate the pitch of written notes (4)
6. In a singing style (9)
10. French term for *slow* (4)
12. Smoothly (6)
14. A form of composition in which one section recurs (5)
15. The French word for *study* (5)
17. A steady rhythm (4)

Lesson 19

Work to do:

Scales/Studies:

Pieces:

Practice record

	MON	TUES	WED	THURS	FRI	SAT	SUN
Scales/Studies							
Pieces							

My comments

Parent's/Carer's comments

Signature_____

*What do you get when you play a
new age song backwards?*
A new age song

Lesson 20

Work to do:

Scales/Studies:

Pieces:

Practice record

	Mon	Tues	Wed	Thurs	Fri	Sat	Sun
Scales/Studies							
Pieces							

My comments

Parent's/Carer's comments

Signature_____

Lesson 21

Work to do:

Scales/Studies:

Pieces:

Practice record

	MON	TUES	WED	THURS	FRI	SAT	SUN
Scales/Studies							
Pieces							

My comments

Parent's/Carer's comments

Signature_____

What do you do when a musician comes to the door?

Give them the money and take the pizza

Lesson 22

Date/Time:

Work to do:

Scales/Studies:

Pieces:

Practice record

	MON	TUES	WED	THURS	FRI	SAT	SUN
Scales/Studies							
Pieces							

My comments

Parent's/Carer's comments

Signature_____

Who invented the 'Do-Re-Mi' scales?
Guido D'Arezzo
(11th-century monk and music theorist)

57

Lesson 23

Date/Time:

Work to do:

Scales/Studies:

Pieces:

Practice record

	MON	TUES	WED	THURS	FRI	SAT	SUN
Scales/Studies							
Pieces							

My comments

Parent's/Carer's comments

Signature_____

Why did the chicken cross the road?

To get away from the orchestra rehearsal

Lesson 24

Work to do:

Scales/Studies:

Pieces:

Practice record

	MON	TUES	WED	THURS	FRI	SAT	SUN
Scales/Studies							
Pieces							

My comments

Parent's/Carer's comments

Signature_____

Who wrote the music to the popular
musical 'West Side Story'?
Leonard Bernstein (1918–1990)

Take A Break!

Spot The Difference

See if you can spot the six differences between the two pictures.

Lesson 25

Work to do:

Scales/Studies:

Pieces:

Practice record

	MON	TUES	WED	THURS	FRI	SAT	SUN
Scales/Studies							
Pieces							

My comments

Parent's/Carer's comments

Signature_____

What do you get after you've run over an army officer with a steam roller?
A flat major

65

Lesson 26

Work to do:

Scales/Studies:

Pieces:

Practice record

	Mon	Tues	Wed	Thurs	Fri	Sat	Sun
Scales/Studies							
Pieces							

My comments

Parent's/Carer's comments

Signature_____

Which famous composer was the
son of a village butcher?
FACT! Antonin Dvořák (1841–1904)

67

Lesson 27

Work to do:

Scales/Studies:

Pieces:

Practice record

	Mon	Tues	Wed	Thurs	Fri	Sat	Sun
Scales/Studies							
Pieces							

My comments

Parent's/Carer's comments

Signature_____

Why was the musician arrested?

Because he was in treble

Lesson 28

Work to do:

Scales/Studies:

Pieces:

Practice record

	MON	TUES	WED	THURS	FRI	SAT	SUN
Scales/Studies							
Pieces							

My comments

Parent's/Carer's comments

Signature_____

In what year was **Top of the Pops** first broadcast on the BBC?

1964

Lesson 29

Work to do:

Scales/Studies:

Pieces:

Practice record

	MON	TUES	WED	THURS	FRI	SAT	SUN
Scales/Studies							
Pieces							

My comments

Parent's/Carer's comments

Signature_____

What did Bach do when he fell off a horse?

He got Bach in the saddle

Lesson 30

Work to do:

Scales/Studies:

Pieces:

Practice record

	MON	TUES	WED	THURS	FRI	SAT	SUN
Scales/Studies							
Pieces							

My comments

Parent's/Carer's comments

Signature_____

Under which pseudonym did Philip Heseltine compose?

Peter Warlock (1894–1930)

Take A Break!

Note Spelling
Fill in the note names to reveal the words...

1.

    _   I   _   _   _   N

2.

    T   R   _ _   L _   _   L   _ _

3.

    _   O   _ _ _ _   T _ _   L _

4.

    _   R   _   N   _ _ _

5.

    _ _ _   U   T   I   _   U   L

6. _ R _ N _ H _ R _ _ _

7. U N I T _ _ S T _ T _ S O F _ M _ R I _ _

8. V _ _ _ T _ _ L _ P _ T _ H

9. _ _ _ _ _ R

10. _ _ R _ _

If you're finding it difficult, turn to the theory pages at the back for help.

Lesson 31

Work to do:

Scales/Studies:

Pieces:

Practice record

	MON	TUES	WED	THURS	FRI	SAT	SUN
Scales/Studies							
Pieces							

My comments

Parent's/Carer's comments

Signature_____

How do you fix a broken tuba?

With a tuba glue

79

Lesson 32

Date/Time:

Work to do:

Scales/Studies:

Pieces:

Practice record

	MON	TUES	WED	THURS	FRI	SAT	SUN
Scales/Studies							
Pieces							

My comments

Parent's/Carer's comments

Signature_____

What is the literal translation of the Japanese word 'Karaoke'?
Empty orchestra

Lesson 33

Date/Time:

Work to do:

Scales/Studies:

Pieces:

Practice record

	MON	TUES	WED	THURS	FRI	SAT	SUN
Scales/Studies							
Pieces							

My comments

Parent's/Carer's comments

Signature_____

Gone Chopin. Bach in a Minuet!

Lesson 34

Work to do:

Scales/Studies:

Pieces:

Practice record

	MON	TUES	WED	THURS	FRI	SAT	SUN
Scales/Studies							
Pieces							

My comments

Parent's/Carer's comments

Signature_____

Which band were the first non-Asian
act to perform in China?
Wham (in April 1985)

FACT!

Lesson 35

Date/Time:

Work to do:

Scales/Studies:

Pieces:

Practice record

	MON	TUES	WED	THURS	FRI	SAT	SUN
Scales/Studies							
Pieces							

My comments

Parent's/Carer's comments

Signature_____

Why do bees hum?

Because they don't know the words

Date/Time:

Work to do:

Scales/Studies:

Pieces:

Practice record

	MON	TUES	WED	THURS	FRI	SAT	SUN
Scales/Studies							
Pieces							

My comments

Parent's/Carer's comments

Signature_____

On his debut album 'For You', how many instruments did Prince play?

27

Extra Practice Records

Because you might need to practise in the holidays.

Date:	Mon	Tues	Wed	Thurs	Fri	Sat	Sun
Work to do							

Date:	Mon	Tues	Wed	Thurs	Fri	Sat	Sun
Work to do							

Date:	Mon	Tues	Wed	Thurs	Fri	Sat	Sun
Work to do							

Date:	Mon	Tues	Wed	Thurs	Fri	Sat	Sun
Work to do							

Date:	Mon	Tues	Wed	Thurs	Fri	Sat	Sun
Work to do							

Date:	Mon	Tues	Wed	Thurs	Fri	Sat	Sun
Work to do							

Comments

Signature_____

Date:	MON	TUES	WED	THURS	FRI	SAT	SUN
Work to do							

Date:	MON	TUES	WED	THURS	FRI	SAT	SUN
Work to do							

Date:	MON	TUES	WED	THURS	FRI	SAT	SUN
Work to do							

Date:	MON	TUES	WED	THURS	FRI	SAT	SUN

Work to do

Date:	MON	TUES	WED	THURS	FRI	SAT	SUN

Work to do

Date:	MON	TUES	WED	THURS	FRI	SAT	SUN

Work to do

Comments

Signature_____

End Of Year Report

Pupil's comments

....

....

....

....

....

Teacher's comments

....

....

....

....

....

....

....

Signature _____

Theory

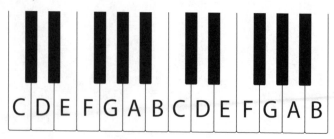

There are seven note names in music – CDEFGAB.

To remember the notes on the lines of the treble clef, think **Every Good Boy Deserves Food.** To remember the notes in the spaces remember **FACE.**

E G B D F   F A C E

To remember the notes on the lines of the bass clef, think **Grizzly Bears Don't Fear Anything.** To remember the notes in the spaces, think **All Cows Eat Grass.**

G B D F A   A C E G

See if you can create your own phrases to help you remember...

Accidentals (alter the pitch of notes)

♯ A **SHARP** raises the pitch of any note by a semitone.

♭ A **FLAT** lowers the pitch of any note by a semitone.

♮ A **NATURAL** cancels out the effect of a sharp or flat.

𝄪 A **DOUBLE SHARP** raises the pitch of any note by a whole tone.

𝄫 A **DOUBLE FLAT** lowers the pitch of any note by a whole tone.

Theory

Note Values

A **SEMIBREVE** (whole note), or rest of equivalent length, lasts for four beats.

A **MINIM** (half note), or rest of equivalent length, lasts for two beats.

A **CROTCHET** (quarter note), or rest of equivalent length, lasts for a quarter of a semibreve and is commonly used as a one-beat note.

A **QUAVER** (eighth note), or rest of equivalent length, lasts for half a beat.

A **SEMIQUAVER** (sixteenth note), or rest of equivalent length, lasts for a quarter of a beat.

A **DEMISEMIQUAVER** (thirty-second note), or rest of equivalent length, lasts for an eighth of a beat.

A **DOT** increases the length of a note or rest by 50%

3 = 2 + 1

A **TIE** joins two notes together – the duration of the second is added to the first.

2½ = 2 + ½

Time Signatures

Simple time

$\frac{2}{4}$ = 2 crotchet beats in a bar.

$\frac{3}{4}$ = 3 crotchet beats in a bar.

$\frac{4}{4}$ = 4 crotchet beats in a bar.

$\frac{3}{2}$ = 3 minim beats in a bar.

Compound time

$\frac{6}{8}$ = 6 quaver beats in a bar.

$\frac{9}{8}$ = 9 quaver beats in a bar.

$\frac{12}{8}$ = 12 quaver beats in a bar.

Unusual time signatures

$\frac{5}{8}$ = 5 quaver beats in a bar.

$\frac{7}{8}$ = 7 quaver beats in a bar.

$\frac{11}{8}$ = 11 quaver beats in a bar.

Theory

Relative Major and Minor Key Signatures

Use this diagram to work out what key a piece of music is in. Look at the key signature of the piece then find it on this page. When practising, try playing the scale of the key you are using to get familiar with the patterns.

Composer Timeline

Era	Renaissance (1450-1600)	Baroque (1600-1750)	Classical (1750-1820)	Romantic (1820-1910)	Modern (1910-present)

Historical markers:
- William Shakespeare (1564-1616)
- Great Fire Of London (1666)
- J.S. Bach (1685-1750)
- St Paul's Cathedral built (1675-1708)
- Wolfgang Amadeus Mozart (1756-1791)
- Ludwig van Beethoven (1770-1827)
- Saxophone invented by Adolphe Sax (1841)
- Pyotr Ilyich Tchaikovsky (1840-1893)
- Sergei Prokofiev (1891-1953)
- The Beatles (1960-1970)

Composers:

- Palestrina (1525-1594)
- Tallis (1505-1585)
- Byrd (1540-1623)
- Allegri (1582-1652)
- Monteverdi (1567-1643)
- Gabrieli (1554-1612)
- Frescobaldi (1583-1643)
- Lassus (1532-1594)
- Schütz (1585-1672)
- Rogier (1561-1596)
- Sweelinck (1562-1621)
- Wert (1535-1596)
- Gesualdo (1566-1613)
- Froberger (1616-1667)
- Lully (1632-1687)
- Buxtehude (1637-1707)
- Pachelbel (1653-1706)
- Corelli (1653-1713)
- Purcell (1659-1695)
- Charpentier (1643-1704)
- Scarlatti (1660-1725)
- Handel (1685-1750)
- Vivaldi (1678-1741)
- Albinoni (1671-1751)
- C.P.E. Bach (1714-1788)
- Telemann (1681-1767)
- Pergolesi (1710-1736)
- Rameau (1683-1764)
- Gluck (1714-1787)
- Haydn (1732-1809)
- Clement (1752-1832)
- Weber (1786-1826)
- Paganini (1782-1840)
- Schubert (1797-1828)
- Rossini (1792-1868)
- Berlioz (1803-1869)
- Wagner (1813-1883)
- Schumann (1810-1856)
- Mendelssohn (1809-1847)
- Chopin (1810-1849)
- Liszt (1811-1886)
- Saint-Saëns (1835-1921)
- Brahms (1833-1897)
- Dvořák (1841-1904)
- Joplin (1868-1917)
- Debussy (1862-1918)
- Elgar (1857-1934)
- Ellington (1899-1974)
- R.V. Williams (1872-1958)
- Rachmaninov (1873-1943)
- Stravinsky (1882-1971)
- Shostakovich (1906-1975)
- Glass (1937-Present)
- Reich (1936-Present)
- Stockhausen (1928-2007)
- Basie (1904-1984)
- Gershwin (1898-1937)
- Bartók (1881-1945)
- Berio (1925-2003)

99

Glossary

Tempo

adagio – Slow, between *andante* and *largo*
allegretto – Moderately fast
allegro – Fast
andante – At walking pace
a tempo – In time, back to the original speed
assai/assez – Very/enough
grave – Slow and solemn
larghetto – Slowly but not as slow as *largo*
largo – Very slowly
lento – Slowly
moderato, modéré – Moderately
presto – Very fast
rallentando, rall. – Getting gradually slower
ritardando, ritard., rit. – Slowing down
ritenuto, riten., rit. – Held back
rubato, tempo rubato – A flexible tempo that can be pulled around to suit the style
stringendo – Pressing forward or moving on
tempo – The speed of a piece of music
vivace – Lively and fast

Italian Terms

cantabile – In a singing style
coda – A closing section added to the end of a piece
da capo, D.C. – To the beginning
dal segno, D.S. – From the sign
dolce – Sweet/gentle
espressivo – Expressive
fine – End
grazioso – Gracefully
legato – Smoothly
maestoso – Majestically, grandly
meno – Less
mezza, mezzo – Half
molto – Very
mosso – With movement
ostinato – A short pattern that is repeated
più – More
poco – A little
staccato, stacc. – Very short notes (articulation) indicated by a dot above the note
subito, sub. – Suddenly
tranquillo – Calm
tremolando, tremolo, trem. – Shaking, fast repetition of the same note or between two or more
troppo – Too much
tutti – All, used to indicate where everyone plays together
vibrato – Repeated slight change in pitch to a single note to make a richer sound

Dynamics

ppp *pianississimo* – As soft as you can

pp *pianissimo* – Very soft

p *piano* – Soft

mp *mezzo-piano* – Moderately soft

mf *mezzo-forte* – Moderately loud

f *forte* – Loud

ff *fortissimo* – Very loud

fff *fortississimo* – As loud as you can

fp *fortepiano* – Loud then immediately soft

sfz, sf *sforzando, sforzato* – A strong accent

crescendo, cresc., cres. – Getting louder

diminuendo, dim. – Getting softer

Other useful terms

Cadenza – A solo section. Often used to show off musical technique within a concerto or similar piece

Chromatic – Moving between notes using only semitone intervals

Concerto – A piece in three parts consisting of a soloist accompanied by an orchestra

Minuet – A piece originally from a dance in triple time

Movement – Section of a large composition (e.g 3rd movement of symphony no. 5)

Octave – An interval of eight notes

Opera – A drama set to music

Overture – A piece used as an introduction to a dramatic, choral or instrumental composition

Pitch – The frequency of a sound

Rhythm – The consequence of a combination of length of notes, articulation and style

Rondo – A musical form in which one section comes back time and time again

Sonata – Instrumental piece for piano, or solo instrument and piano, usually in three movements

Symphony – A large composition for orchestra often in four movements

Symbols

Acciaccatura – A very fast grace note

Appoggiatura – One or more grace notes that uses some value of the note after it (leaning note)

Mordent – An ornament suggesting a quick modification with the note above or below

Pause – Indicates the note or rest should be held longer than usual at the performer's discretion

Slur – Indicates that the notes within it are to be played without separation

Tenuto – Shows the note is to be played slightly longer than usual but not to alter the note value

tr *Trill* – An ornament showing there is to be a rapid alteration with either the note above or below

Turn – A quick alteration between the note above, the note, the note below and the note itself

Clef Practice

Copy the treble clefs below in pencil until you have learned how to draw them. You may have to rub them out and start again for extra practice!

Now try the bass clef...

Notes & Doodles

Notes & Doodles

Notes & Doodles

Notes & Doodles

Manuscript

Take A Break! Answers

Wordsearch

Name That Tune

1. *Away In A Manger*
2. *Danny Boy*
3. *Beethoven – Für Elise*
4. *Rossini – Theme from William Tell Overture*
5. *Parry – Jerusalem*
6. *Scarborough Fair*

Note Spelling

1. *Big Ben*
2. *Treble Clef*
3. *Coffee Table*
4. *Grandad*
5. *Beautiful*
6. *French Bread*

Spot The Difference

Crossword